Table of Contents

Look for the time icon 🕐 for recipes that
cook in 30 minutes or less.

A Handy Guide to Help You Get the Recommended Amount of Fruits and Vegetables

½ cup of vegetables

1 cup of fruit

½ cup of vegetables

½ cup of fruit

¼ cup of dried fruit

½ cup of fruit in 100% fruit juice

½ cup of vegetables

1 cup of raw, leafy greens

Building Healthy Traditions

Family, faith, food, music, art, and dance bind together, forming the soul of the African American. We must also weave good health into our fabric of life. The *Network for a Healthy California—African American Campaign* invites you to take steps to learn about your personal health recommendations and enjoy this cookbook.

Soulful Recipes is full of delicious recipes and tips to help you make eating healthy and being active a part of your family habits. Some recipes are healthy twists on family favorites and some are new foods to try.

You can be a Champion for Change in your family by making new traditions that improve the health of your family. Not sure where to start? Go for the vegetables first. Fill about ½ of your plate with salad and vegetables and then add other foods. Simple changes to the amounts and types of foods you eat can build good, life-long habits for your family.

African Americans suffer from obesity, type 2 diabetes, hypertension, heart disease, and certain types of cancer more than other groups. You can help to prevent and manage these health problems by eating fruits and vegetables and being active. Start your day off right with a healthy breakfast, and pack healthy snacks and lunches to keep you going during the day. If you eat out, choose menu options that are full of fruits and vegetables or ask for fruit instead of dessert. Back at home, make eating dinner together a priority to stay connected. Studies have shown that families that eat together have better nutrition for the whole family.

For more information on the *Network for a Healthy California,* call 1-888-328-3483 or visit us at **www.cachampionsforchange.net.**

Recommended Cups of Fruits and Vegetables

How many cups of fruits and vegetables do you need? It depends on your gender, age, and physical activity level. For more information, visit www.mypyramid.gov.

Girls and Women

Moderate Physical Activity includes walking briskly, hiking, gardening/yard work, and dancing. *Vigorous Physical Activity* includes running/jogging, bicycling, swimming laps, and aerobics.

Physical Activity Level: Moderately or vigorously active for **less than 30 minutes a day**			
Age	**Fruits**	**Vegetables**	**Total**
2-3	1 cup	1 cup	2 cups
4-7	1 cup	1½ cups	2½ cups
8-10	1½ cups	1½ cups	3 cups
11-13	1½ cups	2 cups	3½ cups
14-18	1½ cups	2½ cups	4 cups
19-25	2 cups	2½ cups	4½ cups
26-50	1½ cups	2½ cups	4 cups
51+	1½ cups	2 cups	3½ cups

Physical Activity Level: Moderately or vigorously active for **30 to 60 minutes a day**			
Age	**Fruits**	**Vegetables**	**Total**
2	1 cup	1 cup	2 cups
3	1 cup	1½ cups	2½ cups
4-6	1½ cups	1½ cups	3 cups
7-9	1½ cups	2 cups	3½ cups
10-11	1½ cups	2½ cups	4 cups
12-18	2 cups	2½ cups	4½ cups
19-25	2 cups	3 cups	5 cups
26-50	2 cups	2½ cups	4½ cups
51+	1½ cups	2½ cups	4 cups

Physical Activity Level: Moderately or vigorously active for **more than 60 minutes a day**			
Age	**Fruits**	**Vegetables**	**Total**
2	1 cup	1 cup	2 cups
3-4	1½ cups	1½ cups	3 cups
5-6	1½ cups	2 cups	3½ cups
7-9	1½ cups	2½ cups	4 cups
10-11	2 cups	2½ cups	4½ cups
12-60	2 cups	3 cups	5 cups
61+	2 cups	2½ cups	4½ cups

- To stay healthy and lower the risk of serious health problems, adults need at least 30 minutes of moderate-intensity physical activity every day.

- Children and teenagers need at least 60 minutes of moderate-to-vigorous-intensity physical activity every day.

Recommended Cups of Fruits and Vegetables

How many cups of fruits and vegetables do you need? It depends on your gender, age, and physical activity level. For more information, visit www.mypyramid.gov.

Boys and Men

Moderate Physical Activity includes walking briskly, hiking, gardening/yard work, and dancing. *Vigorous Physical Activity* includes running/jogging, bicycling, swimming laps, and aerobics.

Physical Activity Level: Moderately or vigorously active for **less than 30 minutes a day**

Age	Fruits	Vegetables	Total
2-3	1 cup	1 cup	2 cups
4-5	1 cup	1½ cups	2½ cups
6-8	1½ cups	1½ cups	3 cups
9-10	1½ cups	2 cups	3½ cups
11-12	1½ cups	2½ cups	4 cups
13-14	2 cups	2½ cups	4½ cups
15-18	2 cups	3 cups	5 cups
19-20	2 cups	3½ cups	5½ cups
21-60	2 cups	3 cups	5 cups
61+	2 cups	2½ cups	4½ cups

Physical Activity Level: Moderately or vigorously active for **30 to 60 minutes a day**

Age	Fruits	Vegetables	Total
2	1 cup	1 cup	2 cups
3-5	1½ cups	1½ cups	3 cups
6-8	1½ cups	2 cups	3½ cups
9-10	1½ cups	2½ cups	4 cups
11	2 cups	2½ cups	4½ cups
12-14	2 cups	3 cups	5 cups
15	2 cups	3½ cups	5½ cups
16-25	2½ cups	3½ cups	6 cups
26-45	2 cups	3½ cups	5½ cups
46+	2 cups	3 cups	5 cups

Physical Activity Level: Moderately or vigorously active for **more than 60 minutes a day**

Age	Fruits	Vegetables	Total
2	1 cup	1 cup	2 cups
3	1½ cups	1½ cups	3 cups
4-5	1½ cups	2 cups	3½ cups
6-7	1½ cups	2½ cups	4 cups
8-9	2 cups	2½ cups	4½ cups
10-12	2 cups	3 cups	5 cups
13	2 cups	3½ cups	5½ cups
14	2½ cups	3½ cups	6 cups
15-35	2½ cups	4 cups	6½ cups
36-55	2½ cups	3½ cups	6 cups
56-75	2 cups	3½ cups	5½ cups
76+	2 cups	3 cups	5 cups

- To stay healthy and lower the risk of serious health problems, adults need at least 30 minutes of moderate-intensity physical activity every day.

- Children and teenagers need at least 60 minutes of moderate-to-vigorous-intensity physical activity every day.

Measurement Chart

Dash = ⅛ teaspoon or less

3 teaspoons = 1 tablespoon	1 fluid ounce = 2 tablespoons liquid
2 tablespoons = ⅛ cup	8 fluid ounces = 1 cup
4 tablespoons = ¼ cup	2 cups = 1 pint
5 tablespoons + 1 teaspoon = ⅓ cup	2 pints = 1 quart
8 tablespoons = ½ cup	4 quarts = 1 gallon
16 tablespoons = 1 cup	16 ounces = 1 pound

There are lots of ways to serve fresh fruits and vegetables. If you need to store them for more than a day before serving, follow the storage guidelines below for the best taste and texture.

COUNTERTOP STORAGE

Many fruits and vegetables should be stored only at room temperature because refrigerator temperatures damage them or keep them from ripening to a good flavor and texture. Produce items that should be stored at room temperature include:

Bananas	Honeydew	Oranges	Watermelon	Eggplant	Pumpkin
Cantaloupe	Lemons	Pineapple	Acorn Squash	Jicama	Spaghetti Squash
Grapefruit	Mangos	Plantains	Butternut Squash	Peppers	Tomatoes

RIPEN ON THE COUNTER, AND THEN STORE IN THE REFRIGERATOR

Some produce items continue to ripen after they are picked. If you don't plan on using fruits for a few days, you can buy them while they are firm and ripen at room temperature for a few days and then store in the refrigerator. Produce items that can ripen in a bowl or a paper bag until they reach the desired softness include:

Avocados	Kiwifruit	Nectarines	Peaches	Pears	Plums

CABINET OR PANTRY STORAGE

Produce items that should be stored in a cool, dry, and well-ventilated place, such as in a cabinet or pantry, include:

Onions	Garlic	Potatoes	Sweet Potatoes

REFRIGERATOR STORAGE

Use all refrigerated fruits and vegetables within a few days since longer storage causes loss of flavor and nutrients. Keep fruits separated from vegetables in the refrigerator to prevent over-ripening. Produce items that should be stored in the refrigerator include:

Apples	Figs	Bok Choy	Cauliflower	Greens	Radishes
Apricots	Grapes	Broccoli	Celery	Lettuce	Spinach
Berries	Artichokes	Brussels Sprouts	Corn	Mushrooms	Sprouts
Cherries	Asparagus	Cabbage	Green Beans	Okra	Yellow Squash
Cucumbers	Beets	Carrots	Green Onions	Peas	Zucchini

KEEP IT SAFE!

- In the grocery cart and at home, keep produce separated from raw meat, poultry, and seafood.

- At home, store all fresh-cut and ready-to-eat produce in the refrigerator to keep it cold.

- Keep produce stored on the countertop away from direct sunlight to prevent flavor and nutrient loss.

- Signs of spoilage include bad odor, discoloration, mold, and mushy texture.

- Wash all whole fruits and vegetables just before eating, including items with thick skins like melons.

For more information on fruits and vegetables, refer to the Produce Quick Tips at **www.cachampionsforchange.net.**

Postharvest Technology Research & Information Center, University of California, Davis, Division of Agriculture and Natural Resources

INTRODUCTION (8)

Herbs and Spices

What makes food delicious? Flavor. Herbs and spices are key ingredients that add flavor to your food. You can use fresh or dried herbs and spices or try using mixtures to create a variety of tasty new flavors for foods you usually eat.

DID YOU KNOW?

- Herbs and spices are calorie free.

- Using herbs and spices will help you cook with more flavor, using less fat, salt, and sugar.

- Lower the cost of herbs and spices by growing your own in a container or backyard garden.

- Try the "ethnic" food isle at your grocery store for low-cost bags of dried herbs and spices.

- Use the herbs, spices, and mixtures below to add flavor to your dishes:

"*Afternoon in the Park*" – *Michael Cunningham*

Desserts	Savory	Spicy
Allspice	Basil	Black pepper
Cinnamon	Cumin	Cayenne pepper
Ginger	Garlic	Chili powder
Nutmeg	Oregano	Paprika
Vanilla	Rosemary	
	Sage	
	Thyme	

Breakfast Recipes

Activities like jumping rope, jogging, or even walking also help your body turn calcium into strong bones.

Calcium is a mineral that is important to the overall health of your body. For most people, dairy foods are the major source of calcium in the diet. However, some fruits and vegetables also contain calcium such as, collard greens, spinach, broccoli, and calcium-fortified 100% orange juice.

BENEFITS OF CALCIUM:

- It helps to build and maintain strong bones.

- It may help lower the risk of high blood pressure.

- It helps your muscles contract and heart to beat.

TRY THIS!

- For breakfast eat a cup of lowfat yogurt with fruit.

- Eat a spinach salad with two tablespoons of lowfat salad dressing for lunch.

- Make smoothies with calcium-fortified 100% fruit juice or yogurt.

DO YOU HAVE DISCOMFORT AFTER DRINKING MILK OR EATING DAIRY PRODUCTS?

If you do, you may have lactose intolerance. If you have problems digesting milk and other dairy products, try smaller amounts with meals, lactose-free milk, natural aged or ripened cheeses such as Swiss and Cheddar, or yogurt with active cultures. Always consult your physician to be sure you have lactose intolerance.

Strawberry Smoothie

A cool start to your active day or an afternoon pick-me-up.

Mango Smoothie

A tropical twist for your morning.

 Makes 3 servings.
1 cup per serving.
Prep time: 10 minutes

INGREDIENTS

½ cup 100% orange juice

1 large banana, peeled and sliced

1 cup fresh or frozen strawberries, thawed

1 cup lowfat vanilla yogurt

5 ice cubes

PREPARATION

1. Combine orange juice, banana, and half the strawberries into a blender container. Blend until smooth.

2. Add yogurt, remaining strawberries, and ice cubes. Blend until smooth. Serve immediately.

Nutrition information per serving: Calories 153, Carbohydrate 32 g, Dietary Fiber 3 g, Protein 5 g, Total Fat 1 g, Saturated Fat 1 g, Trans Fat 0 g, Cholesterol 4 mg, Sodium 57 mg

 Makes 4 servings.
1 cup per serving.
Prep time: 10 minutes

INGREDIENTS

1 cup 100% orange juice

1 small banana, peeled and sliced

2 fresh mangos, peeled and chopped or 2½ cups frozen mango chunks, thawed

5 ice cubes

PREPARATION

1. Combine orange juice, banana, and half the mango into a blender container. Blend until smooth.

2. Add remaining mango and ice cubes. Blend until smooth. Serve immediately.

Nutrition information per serving: Calories 120, Carbohydrate 30 g, Dietary Fiber 3 g, Protein 1 g, Total Fat 0 g, Saturated Fat 0 g, Trans Fat 0 g, Cholesterol 0 mg, Sodium 4 mg

Adapted from recipe courtesy of BOND of Color.

Adapted from recipe courtesy of BOND of Color.

Veggie Scramble Wraps

Great for breakfast on the go. Make it your way by using your favorite mix of vegetables.

INGREDIENTS

nonstick cooking spray

1 cup chopped fresh or frozen vegetables (bell peppers, onions, broccoli, and mushrooms)

1 cup egg substitute

2 (6-inch) flour tortillas

¼ cup grated lowfat Cheddar cheese

PREPARATION

1. Spray a medium skillet with nonstick cooking spray and heat over medium heat.

2. Cook vegetables until tender, about 5 minutes.

3. Add egg substitute and stir until thoroughly cooked, about 5 minutes.

4. Warm the tortillas in the microwave for 5 to 10 seconds.

5. Place half of the egg mixture in each tortilla and sprinkle with cheese.

6. Wrap the tortilla around the egg mixture and enjoy.

Makes 2 servings. *1 wrap per serving.*
Prep time: 5 minutes **Cook time:** 10 minutes

Nutrition information per serving: Calories 191, Carbohydrate 19 g, Dietary Fiber 4 g, Protein 21 g, Total Fat 4 g, Saturated Fat 1 g, Trans Fat 0 g, Cholesterol 3 mg, Sodium 537 mg

Turkey Apple Sausage Breakfast Sandwiches

Get a head start on dinner! Set aside 2 sausage patties to make the Dirty Rice and Blackeye Peas recipe from page 32.

INGREDIENTS

Turkey Apple Sausage

- 1 pound ground turkey
- 1 red delicious apple, peeled, cored, and chopped
- 2 large cloves garlic, finely chopped and divided into 2 portions
- ½ teaspoon dried thyme
- ¼ teaspoon red pepper flakes
- 1 teaspoon dried sage
- ¼ teaspoon ground black pepper
- ⅛ teaspoon ground coriander
- nonstick cooking spray

Breakfast Sandwich

- 2½ cups chopped mushrooms
- 1½ cups chopped onions
- 6 whole wheat English muffins
- 6 slices tomato

PREPARATION

1. In a large bowl, combine turkey, apple, one garlic clove, thyme, red pepper flakes, sage, ground black pepper, and coriander; mix well.

2. Form the turkey mixture into 8 patties (set aside 2 patties for the Dirty Rice and Blackeye Peas recipe on page 32).

3. Spray a large skillet with nonstick cooking spray and heat over medium heat.

4. Cook patties until they are cooked through, about 5 to 7 minutes per side. Set aside.

5. Spray the skillet with nonstick cooking spray and sauté the remaining garlic for 3 minutes.

continued on following page

Makes 6 servings. *1 patty per serving.*
Prep time: 5 minutes **Cook time:** 25 minutes

Nutrition information per serving: Calories 256, Carbohydrate 35 g, Dietary Fiber 6 g, Protein 19 g, Total Fat 5 g, Saturated Fat 1 g, Trans Fat 0 g, Cholesterol 38 mg, Sodium 459 mg

Turkey Apple Sausage Breakfast Sandwiches *(continued)*

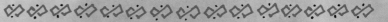

PREPARATION

6. Add mushrooms and onions. Sauté until the mushrooms are tender and onions begin to brown, about 5 minutes.

7. Cut each English muffin in half. Place a Turkey Apple Sausage patty, ⅓ cup of mushroom-onion mixture, and a slice of tomato on 6 English muffin halves.

8. Cover each sandwich with the other English muffin half and enjoy!

 Makes 6 servings. *1 patty per serving.*
Prep time: 5 minutes **Cook time:** 25 minutes

Nutrition information per serving: Calories 256, Carbohydrate 35 g, Dietary Fiber 6 g, Protein 19 g, Total Fat 5 g, Saturated Fat 1 g, Trans Fat 0 g, Cholesterol 38 mg, Sodium 459 mg

Turkey Apple Sausage recipe courtesy of BOND of Color.

Sweet Potato Hash

This savory and sweet side dish is sure to be a breakfast favorite.

INGREDIENTS

¼ cup vegetable oil

2 cups frozen or fresh chopped bell peppers and onions

2 pounds sweet potatoes (about 2 medium sweet potatoes), peeled and cut into small cubes

1 teaspoon cumin

1 teaspoon salt

1 teaspoon red pepper flakes

PREPARATION

1. Heat oil in a large skillet over medium-high heat.

2. Sauté bell peppers and onions until tender, about 5 minutes.

3. Add remaining ingredients and reduce heat to medium.

4. Cook for 20 to 25 minutes, stirring every 2 to 3 minutes. Sweet potatoes may begin to stick to the skillet, but continue to stir gently until they cook through. Serve while hot.

 Makes 6 servings. *1 cup per serving.*
Prep time: 10 minutes **Cook time:** 30 minutes

Nutrition information per serving: Calories 244, Carbohydrate 38 g, Dietary Fiber 4 g, Protein 3 g, Total Fat 9 g, Saturated Fat 1 g, Trans Fat 0 g, Cholesterol 0 mg, Sodium 407 mg

Spotlight On: African American Cuisine

For centuries, African American cooks have lovingly prepared family meals using the ingredients available from their gardens. Farming traditions, both in the United States and the African homelands, made local fruits and vegetables the main ingredients in the foods served at home. Now more than ever, African Americans need to regain that tradition. Cooking with fruits and vegetables not only improves the health of African Americans, but ensures that this culinary heritage continues.

Boston Organization of Nutritionists and Dietitians of Color (BOND) was formed in 1995 by African American and Afro Caribbean nutritionists and dietitians in the Greater Boston area. Its mission is to support healthy eating and wellness in minority communities. BOND also mentors and encourages fellow professionals to support future minority students to enter the fields of nutrition and wellness.

See the following recipes contributed by BOND of Color:

Strawberry Smoothie on page 13

Mango Smoothie on page 13

Turkey Apple Sausage Breakfast Sandwiches on pages 15–16

Two Bean and Corn Salad on page 23

Rainbow Coleslaw on page 25

Soulful Seasoning on page 34

One Pot Vegetarian Stew on page 40

Nellie's Kale Stew on page 55

Honey Gingered Fruit Salad on page 60

Vegetable Brunch Pie

Who knew your children could love eating cauliflower?

INGREDIENTS

nonstick cooking spray

2¼ cups chopped cauliflower florets

1 tablespoon vegetable oil

1 medium onion, chopped

1 (8-ounce) package mushrooms, sliced

4½ cups (about 6 ounces) of beet, mustard, or collard greens, finely chopped

½ teaspoon garlic powder

½ teaspoon onion powder

1 teaspoon brown sugar

½ teaspoon salt

⅛ teaspoon ground cayenne pepper

¾ cup shredded lowfat Cheddar cheese

1 cup lowfat milk

¾ cup egg substitute

¾ cup baking mix

PREPARATION

1. Place an oven rack in the middle of the oven. Preheat oven to 375°F.

2. Spray a 10-inch pie dish with nonstick cooking spray and set aside.

3. In a microwave safe bowl, microwave cauliflower on high for 3 minutes, or steam it on the stovetop.

4. Pour vegetable oil into a 12-inch skillet and heat over medium heat.

5. Sauté onion and mushrooms until tender, about 5 minutes.

6. Add greens, garlic powder, onion powder, brown sugar, salt, and cayenne pepper. Sauté for another 3 minutes until greens are wilted.

7. Stir the cooked cauliflower into the greens mixture and place in the pie dish. Sprinkle with cheese.

8. In a medium bowl, combine milk, egg substitute, and baking mix. Whisk until well blended and pour over vegetable mixture.

9. Bake 30 to 35 minutes or until golden brown. Serve while hot.

Adapted from recipe courtesy of Cut 'n Clean Greens.

Makes 8 servings. *4-inch slice per serving.*
Prep time: 15 minutes **Cook time:** 50 minutes

Nutrition information per serving:, Calories 128, Carbohydrate 15 g, Dietary Fiber 3 g, Protein 9 g, Total Fat 5 g, Saturated Fat 1 g, Trans Fat 0 g, Cholesterol 4 mg, Sodium 537 mg

Mushroom Quiche

Serve this dish with whole wheat toast and 100% orange juice for a balanced start to your day.

INGREDIENTS

nonstick cooking spray

1¼ cups sliced mushrooms

3 green onions, finely chopped

1 clove garlic, finely chopped

1½ teaspoons dried oregano

2 teaspoons dried basil

¼ teaspoon salt

1 teaspoon dried marjoram

¼ teaspoon dried thyme

¼ teaspoon ground black pepper

½ teaspoon dried mustard

1 cup egg substitute

¾ cup nonfat milk

½ cup shredded lowfat Cheddar cheese

PREPARATION

1. Place an oven rack in the lower third of the oven. Preheat oven to 375°F.

2. Spray a large skillet with nonstick cooking spray and heat over medium-high heat.

3. Sauté mushrooms, green onions, and garlic until tender, about 5 minutes.

4. Stir in oregano, basil, salt, marjoram, thyme, ground black pepper, and dry mustard. Cook until liquid is evaporated, about 2 minutes.

5. Let the mushroom mixture cool for about 5 minutes.

6. In a medium bowl, combine egg substitute, milk, and cheese; beat well.

7. Combine the batter with the mushroom mixture and pour into a 10-inch pie dish.

8. Bake for 35 to 45 minutes until filling is puffed, set, and starting to brown. Serve while hot.

Makes 6 servings. *4-inch slice per serving.*
Prep time: 15 minutes **Cook time:** 1 hour

Nutrition information per serving: Calories 58, Carbohydrate 4 g, Dietary Fiber 1 g, Protein 8 g, Total Fat 1 g, Saturated Fat 0 g, Trans Fat 0 g, Cholesterol 3 mg, Sodium 280 mg

Side Dish Recipes

Dance has always been part of African culture, connecting families to cultural traditions, expressing emotions from faith to joy, and simply celebrating good times. Dancing can get your whole body moving. You can sway to the music in a slow flow or pick up the pace for a high energy dance groove. No matter what age or stage of life you are in, dancing can be a daily practice. Dancing is physical activity and you can reap the benefits of being active while having fun by yourself or with family and friends.

BENEFITS

- Dancing can help build cardiovascular and muscle strength.

- The more you dance and move your body the more calories you burn, helping you to lose weight or keep it off.

- Dancing lowers stress and boosts your energy to help you make it through your week.

- It lowers blood pressure and the risk for heart disease.

TRY THIS!

- You can dance wherever you are, no equipment necessary, just turn on your favorite music and go.

- Dance your way to fitness. Move around the house to the beat as you do your household cleaning like vacuuming, dusting, or washing and putting away clothes.

- Check your local community center for a dance class. Learn hip-hop moves, jazz dance, line dancing, gospel aerobics, or traditional African dance.

Two Bean and Corn Salad

Try this salad as a condiment on grilled fish and chicken dishes.

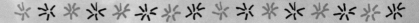

INGREDIENTS

⅓ cup vegetable oil

2 tablespoons balsamic vinaigrette

1 teaspoon cumin

1 (15-ounce) can black beans, drained and rinsed

1 (15-ounce) can Great Northern beans, drained and rinsed

3 stalks celery, chopped

2 cups frozen corn, thawed

1 medium red bell pepper, chopped

1 cup chopped red onion

⅓ cup chopped fresh cilantro

2 small jalapeño peppers, seeded and chopped (optional)

PREPARATION

1. In a large bowl, whisk oil, vinegar, and cumin.

2. Add remaining ingredients and toss to coat.

3. Serve immediately or refrigerate for up to 1 hour to allow flavors to blend.

 Makes 10 servings. *1 cup per serving.*
Prep time: 10 minutes

Nutrition information per serving: Calories 227, Carbohydrate 31 g, Dietary Fiber 9 g, Protein 9 g, Total Fat 8 g, Saturated Fat 1 g, Trans Fat 0 g, Cholesterol 0 mg, Sodium 334 mg

Super Salad Toppers

Salad shy? There is something for everyone with these simple sides.

INGREDIENTS

5 cups chopped salad greens (romaine, red or green leaf lettuce, spinach, spring mix, or a combination)

Citrus Splash Mix-In

1 large orange, peeled and cut into sections

1 medium pink or red grapefruit, peeled and cut into sections

½ cup chopped red onion

1 cup thinly sliced radishes

¼ cup sliced almonds

2 tablespoons light sesame dressing

2 tablespoons 100% orange juice

Nutrition information per serving: Calories 136, Carbohydrate 21 g, Dietary Fiber 5 g, Protein 4 g, Total Fat 6 g, Saturated Fat 1 g, Trans Fat 0 g, Cholesterol 0 mg, Sodium 112 mg

Savory & Satisfying Mix-In

1 cup canned black beans, drained and rinsed

½ red bell pepper, chopped

1 tomato, chopped

1 cup sweet corn

4 tablespoons lowfat Ranch dressing

Nutrition information per serving: Calories 151, Carbohydrate 27 g, Dietary Fiber 8 g, Protein 6 g, Total Fat 3 g, Saturated Fat 0 g, Trans Fat 0 g, Cholesterol 3 mg, Sodium 331 mg

Sweet Sensation Mix-In

1 cup sliced strawberries

1 cup shredded carrots

1 cup sliced apples

½ cup raisins

4 tablespoons lowfat balsamic vinaigrette

Nutrition information per serving: Calories 130, Carbohydrate 28 g, Dietary Fiber 4 g, Protein 2 g, Total Fat 2 g, Saturated Fat 0 g, Trans Fat 0 g, Cholesterol 0 mg, Sodium 252 mg

PREPARATION

1. Place salad greens in a large bowl.

2. Choose one of the Mix-Ins listed above and combine with the salad greens.

3. Toss all ingredients together and serve immediately.

Makes 4 servings. *2 cups per serving.*
Prep time: 10 minutes

Rainbow Coleslaw

Pack with Oven Fried Chicken for a tasty picnic lunch.

✳ ✳ ✳ ✳ ✳ ✳ ✳ ✳ ✳ ✳ ✳ ✳ ✳ ✳ ✳ ✳

INGREDIENTS

2 cups thinly sliced red cabbage

2 cups thinly sliced green cabbage

½ cup chopped yellow or red bell pepper

½ cup shredded carrots

⅓ cup chopped red onion

½ cup fat free mayonnaise

1 tablespoon red wine vinegar

¼ teaspoon celery seed (optional)

½ cup lowfat Cheddar cheese, cut into bite-size cubes

PREPARATION

1. In a large bowl, combine all the vegetables.

2. In a small bowl, mix mayonnaise, vinegar, and celery seed (if desired) to make a dressing.

3. Pour the dressing over the vegetable mixture and toss until well coated.

4. Toss salad with cheese and serve chilled.

 Makes 12 servings. *½ cup per serving.*
Prep time: 15 minutes

Nutrition information per serving: Calories 30, Carbohydrate 4 g, Dietary Fiber 1 g, Protein 2 g, Total Fat 1 g, Saturated Fat 0 g, Trans Fat 0 g, Cholesterol 2 mg, Sodium 145 mg

Adapted from recipe courtesy of BOND of Color.

Spotlight On: Blackeye Peas

Blackeye peas originated in Africa and are one of the most ancient vegetables. Although they are a Southern favorite, more blackeye peas are grown in California than in any other state.

One cup of cooked blackeye peas is an excellent source of fiber, iron, vitamin K, thiamin, folate, and magnesium. One cup of cooked blackeye peas is also a source of zinc and potassium.

Blackeye peas are just one example of the many African American Southern style foods that are jam-packed with nutrients but often cooked in an unhealthy way. Enjoy the natural flavors of your blackeye peas, greens, sweet potatoes, squash, and okra with the delicious and healthy recipes found in these pages.

For more recipes on Southern style foods, visit Glory Foods at www.gloryfoods.com.

See the following recipes contributed by Glory Foods:

Mango and Blackeye Pea Salsa on page 27

Sweet Potato Apple Bake on page 64

Mango and Blackeye Pea Salsa

Serve with grilled fish or chicken.

INGREDIENTS

1 (15½-ounce) can blackeye peas, drained and rinsed

1½ tomatoes, finely chopped

1 mango, peeled and finely chopped

2 green onions, chopped

1 tablespoon vegetable oil

1 tablespoon white vinegar

juice of half a lime

1 teaspoon ground cumin

½ teaspoon garlic powder

PREPARATION

1. In a large bowl, combine all ingredients and mix well.

2. Serve immediately or cover and refrigerate for up to 4 hours to allow the flavors to blend.

3. Serve with baked pita or corn chips.

 Makes 10 servings. *½ cup per serving.*
Prep time: 15 minutes

Nutrition information per serving: Calories 83, Carbohydrate 14 g, Dietary Fiber 3 g, Protein 4 g, Total Fat 2 g, Saturated Fat 0 g, Trans Fat 0 g, Cholesterol 0 mg, Sodium 108 mg

Adapted from recipe courtesy of Glory Foods.

Herbed Potato Salad

Fresh vegetables and a light vinaigrette give this salad a lively flavor.

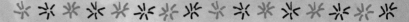

INGREDIENTS

1½ pounds red potatoes (about 8 potatoes), cut into cubes

½ cup light Italian dressing

½ tablespoon spicy brown mustard

1 tablespoon chopped fresh parsley

1 teaspoon garlic salt

¼ teaspoon ground black pepper

½ cup chopped red bell pepper

½ cup chopped green bell pepper

½ cup chopped green onions

PREPARATION

1. In a large pot, cook potatoes in boiling water until tender, about 10 minutes (do not overcook).

2. Drain well and let cool.

3. Cut potatoes into bite-size pieces and place in a medium bowl.

4. In a small bowl, combine dressing, mustard, parsley, and seasonings; pour over potatoes and toss well.

5. Carefully stir in bell peppers and green onions. Cover and chill until ready to serve.

 Makes 6 servings. *½ cup per serving.*
Prep time: 10 minutes **Cook time:** 10 minutes

Nutrition information per serving: Calories 132, Carbohydrate 24 g, Dietary Fiber 4 g, Protein 2 g, Total Fat 4 g, Saturated Fat 1 g, Trans Fat 0 g, Cholesterol 0 mg, Sodium 441 mg

Creole Green Beans

Spice up your everyday dinners with this jazzy dish.

INGREDIENTS

2 teaspoons vegetable oil

2 small cloves garlic, chopped

1 (16-ounce) package frozen cut green beans

1 cup chopped red bell pepper

1 cup chopped fresh tomatoes

½ cup chopped celery

½ teaspoon salt

¼ teaspoon cayenne pepper

PREPARATION

1. Heat oil in a large skillet over low heat.

2. Sauté garlic in oil for 1 minute.

3. Add green beans and bell peppers; increase heat to medium and cook for 7 minutes.

4. Stir in tomatoes, celery, and seasonings; cook for 7 minutes more. Serve while hot.

 Makes 8 servings. *1 cup per serving.*
Prep time: 10 minutes **Cook time:** 15 minutes

Nutrition information per serving: Calories 35, Carbohydrate 6 g, Dietary Fiber 2 g, Protein 1 g, Total Fat 1 g, Saturated Fat 0 g, Trans Fat 0 g, Cholesterol 0 mg, Sodium 159 mg

Sweet Potato Fries

A delightful surprise for kids who love fries!

INGREDIENTS

nonstick cooking spray

1 large sweet potato, peeled

¼ cup egg substitute

1 teaspoon nutmeg

PREPARATION

1. Place an oven rack in the middle of the oven. Preheat oven to 425°F.

2. Spray a baking sheet with nonstick cooking spray and set aside.

3. Slice the sweet potato into ½-inch thick fries and place in a medium bowl.

4. Pour egg substitute over the sweet potato fries and sprinkle nutmeg on top; toss until well coated.

5. Place the sweet potato fries on the baking sheet so that they do not touch.

6. Bake until the edges of the potatoes start to turn crispy and brown, about 25 minutes.

7. Remove fries from the oven and serve while hot.

 Makes 2 servings. *½ potato per serving.*
Prep time: 10 minutes **Cook time:** 25 minutes

Nutrition information per serving: Calories 109, Carbohydrate 20 g, Dietary Fiber 3 g, Protein 5 g, Total Fat 1 g, Saturated Fat 0 g, Trans Fat 0 g, Cholesterol 0 mg, Sodium 90 mg

Savory Greens

Make this Sunday dinner dish pop with hot sauce.

INGREDIENTS

3 cups water

¼ pound skinless, smoked turkey breast

¼ cup chopped onion

1 tablespoon chopped and seeded jalapeño pepper (optional)

2 cloves garlic, crushed

¼ teaspoon cayenne pepper

¼ teaspoon ground cloves

½ teaspoon dried thyme

1 green onion, chopped

1 teaspoon ground ginger

2 pounds greens (mixture of mustard greens, collard greens, kale, and turnip greens)

PREPARATION

1. Place all ingredients except greens into a large pot and bring to a boil.

2. Prepare greens by washing thoroughly and removing stems.

3. Tear or slice greens into bite-size pieces.

4. Add greens to turkey stock. Cook 20 to 30 minutes until tender. Serve while hot.

 Makes 6 servings. *1 cup per serving.*
Prep time: 10 minutes **Cook time:** 30 minutes

Nutrition information per serving: Calories 69, Carbohydrate 10 g, Dietary Fiber 4 g, Protein 7 g, Total Fat 1 g, Saturated Fat 0 g, Trans Fat 0 g, Cholesterol 9 mg, Sodium 267 mg

Adapted from recipe courtesy of National Heart Lung and Blood Institute.

Dirty Rice and Blackeye Peas

The sausage in this dish also makes a lean and healthy option for breakfast.

❋ ❋ ❋ ❋ ❋ ❋ ❋ ❋ ❋ ❋ ❋ ❋ ❋ ❋ ❋ ❋

INGREDIENTS

2½ cups fat free, low-sodium vegetable broth

2 bay leaves

1¾ cups long grain rice

2 cups frozen blackeye peas
nonstick cooking spray

1 cup finely chopped onion

1 cup finely chopped celery

½ cup finely chopped bell pepper

1 tablespoon Soulful Seasoning (see recipe on page 34)

6 ounces (about 2 patties) Turkey Apple Sausage (see recipe on pages 15–16)

2 cloves garlic, finely chopped

½ tablespoon dried parsley

½ teaspoon dried oregano

PREPARATION

1. In a large skillet, combine vegetable broth and bay leaves; bring to a boil.

2. Add rice and blackeye peas to broth and cover.

3. Reduce heat to simmer until all liquid is absorbed, about 18 to 20 minutes.

4. Remove bay leaves and place cooked rice and blackeye peas in a large bowl.

5. Spray a nonstick skillet with cooking spray and heat over medium-high heat. Add onion, celery, bell pepper, Soulful Seasoning, Turkey Apple Sausage, garlic, parsley, and oregano.

6. Sauté until sausage is thoroughly cooked, about 5 minutes.

7. Combine with rice and blackeye pea mixture. Serve while hot.

Makes 9 servings. *1 cup per serving.*
Prep time: 10 minutes **Cook time:** 30 minutes

Nutrition information per serving: Calories 207, Carbohydrate 40 g, Dietary Fiber 3 g, Protein 8 g, Total Fat 1 g, Saturated Fat 0 g, Trans Fat 0 g, Cholesterol 8 mg, Sodium 85 mg

Roasted Vegetable Medley

Bring harmony to your taste buds with this fresh vegetable dish. Add a Southern flair by serving over grits!

INGREDIENTS

nonstick cooking spray

1 cup chopped baby carrots

1 cup chopped eggplant

1 cup chopped asparagus

1 teaspoon vegetable oil

2 cloves garlic, chopped

4 teaspoons dried basil

1 cup chopped mushrooms

1 small zucchini, chopped

PREPARATION

1. Place an oven rack on the bottom of the oven. Preheat oven to 450°F.

2. Spray a roasting pan with nonstick cooking spray.

3. Add carrots, eggplant, and asparagus to the pan. Drizzle with vegetable oil and toss until vegetables are lightly coated.

4. Bake for 20 minutes.

5. Spray a large pan with nonstick cooking spray and heat over medium heat.

6. Sauté garlic and basil for about 2 minutes.

7. Add mushrooms and zucchini and sauté until vegetables are tender, about 5 minutes.

8. Add roasted vegetables to the pan and sauté 5 minutes more. Serve immediately.

Makes 4 servings. *1 cup per serving.*
Prep time: 15 minutes **Cook time:** 35 minutes

Nutrition information per serving: Calories 50, Carbohydrate 8 g, Dietary Fiber 3 g, Protein 2 g, Total Fat 2 g, Saturated Fat 0 g, Trans Fat 0 g, Cholesterol 0 mg, Sodium 26 mg

Soulful Seasoning

Add flavor to soups, stews, and side dishes with this savory seasoning.

INGREDIENTS

3 tablespoons onion powder

4 tablespoons garlic powder

1 tablespoon ground red pepper

1 tablespoon chili powder

1 tablespoon paprika

1 teaspoon ground black pepper

2 teaspoon ground thyme

PREPARATION

1. Mix all ingredients together to make ¾ cup seasoning.

2. Store in an airtight container and use in place of seasoning salts.

See the following recipes that use Soulful Seasoning:
Dirty Rice and Blackeye Peas on page 32
Sautéed Okra with Onions and Tomatoes on page 39
Catfish Stew on page 41
Oven Fried Catfish with Stir-Fry Greens on page 46

Makes 12 servings. *1 tablespoon per serving.*
Prep time: 5 minutes

Nutrition information per serving: Calories 0, Carbohydrate 0 g,
Dietary Fiber 0 g, Protein 0 g, Total Fat 0 g, Saturated Fat 0 g,
Trans Fat 0 g, Cholesterol 0 mg, Sodium 0 mg

Recipe courtesy of BOND of Color.

Supreme Mashed Potatoes

Think your kids won't like orange mashed potatoes? Try using parsnips in place of carrots. They are white like potatoes and sweet like carrots.

✴ ✴ ✴ ✴ ✴ ✴ ✴ ✴ ✴ ✴ ✴ ✴ ✴ ✴ ✴

INGREDIENTS

6 medium baking potatoes, peeled and cut into chunks

2 large carrots, peeled and chopped

3 large cloves garlic, finely chopped

½ cup low-sodium chicken broth

1 tablespoon butter

PREPARATION

1. Combine potatoes and carrots in a large pot and fill with cold water. Bring to a boil and cook 5 minutes.

2. Add garlic and reduce heat to simmer until potatoes and carrots are tender, about 35 minutes.

3. Drain and keep 1 cup of the cooking liquid.

4. Mash the potatoes and carrots with a hand masher.

5. Combine chicken broth and butter in a small pan; heat over medium heat until the butter melts.

6. Slowly stir broth mixture into the mashed potatoes and carrots.

7. If necessary, add the reserved cooking liquid until the potatoes reach the desired thickness. Serve while hot.

Makes 10 servings. *¾ cup per serving.*
Prep time: 10 minutes **Cook time:** 45 minutes

Nutrition information per serving: Calories 104, Carbohydrate 22 g, Dietary Fiber 2 g, Protein 2 g, Total Fat 1 g, Saturated Fat 1 g, Trans Fat 0 g, Cholesterol 3 mg, Sodium 51 mg

Main Dish Recipes

Southern Fried Chicken. Collard Greens. Blackeye Peas. Cornbread. Sweet Potato Pie. When you think of these foods, you may think of grandma cooking in her kitchen on Sunday. Sunday dinner is a big part of African American culture. It brings families home for more than just eating soul food. It is a time when families come together to enjoy cooking, sharing stories, and playing games.

Families today are still getting together for Sunday dinner. But, mothers are changing the way they make 'grandma's' recipes. Today, many African American moms know that there is a link between what we eat and why so many of us suffer from serious health problems like obesity, type 2 diabetes, heart disease, stroke, and certain types of cancer.

Moms are taking control of their kitchens and their communities. They are talking with their friends, store owners, and community leaders about getting healthy food in their neighborhoods. They are changing their way of cooking soul food, just enough, so that it is *still* delicious – just healthy.

Try the meals on the right for your next Sunday dinner. They are healthier versions of traditional favorites that taste great. All you have to add is love and care to make them special to your family. Be a Champion for Change in your family. Inspire healthy change with the foods you cook and the stories you share at the dinner table.

Fresh and Delightful

Oven Fried Catfish with
  Stir-Fry Greens
Herbed Potato Salad
Honey Gingered Fruit Salad

Nutrition information per serving:
Calories 513, Carbohydrate 82 g,
Dietary Fiber 11 g, Protein 26 g,
Total Fat 11 g, Saturated Fat 2 g, Trans Fat 0 g,
Cholesterol 57 mg, Sodium 542 mg

Family Favorites

Oven Fried Chicken and
  Summer Squash
Rainbow Coleslaw
Sweet Potato Apple Bake

Nutrition information per serving:
Calories 337, Carbohydrate 46 g,
Dietary Fiber 7 g, Protein 24 g,
Total Fat 8 g, Saturated Fat 3 g, Trans Fat 0 g,
Cholesterol 54 mg, Sodium 384 mg

Simple Supper

Cornbread with Spicy
  Blackeye Peas
Savory Greens
Oven Fried Plantains

Nutrition information per serving:
Calories 556, Carbohydrate 106 g,
Dietary Fiber 14 g, Protein 19 g,
Total Fat 9 g, Saturated Fat 1 g, Trans Fat 0 g,
Cholesterol 34 mg, Sodium 478 mg

Sautéed Okra with Onions and Tomatoes

Share this hearty vegetarian meal at your next potluck.

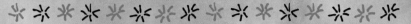

INGREDIENTS

- 2 teaspoons vegetable oil
- 1 small onion, chopped
- 1 pound okra, ends trimmed, rinsed, and cut into ½-inch thick slices or 1 (16-ounce) package frozen okra
- 1 (14½-ounce) can diced tomatoes

- 1 teaspoon Soulful Seasoning (see recipe on page 34)
- ½ teaspoon hot sauce
- ¼ teaspoon ground black pepper
- 2 cups cooked brown rice

PREPARATION

1. Heat oil in a large skillet over medium-high heat.

2. Sauté onion until tender, about 3 minutes.

3. Add remaining ingredients and cook, stirring frequently, until okra is slightly tender, but not mushy, about 5 minutes.

4. Serve 1 cup of sautéed okra over ½ cup of brown rice.

Makes 4 servings. *1½ cups per serving.*
Prep time: 10 minutes **Cook time:** 10 minutes

Nutrition information per serving: Calories 182, Carbohydrate 34 g, Dietary Fiber 7 g, Protein 6 g, Total Fat 4 g, Saturated Fat 0 g, Trans Fat 0 g, Cholesterol 0 mg, Sodium 144 mg

One Pot Vegetarian Stew

Warm up your winter evenings with this hearty vegetable dish.

INGREDIENTS

2 teaspoons vegetable oil

1 medium onion, chopped

1 medium green bell pepper, chopped

3 cloves garlic, finely chopped

1 (14½-ounce) can diced tomatoes

2 cups fresh or frozen corn

1 (14½-ounce) can low-sodium vegetable broth

2 teaspoons chili powder

2 teaspoons dried oregano

1 (15-ounce) can black beans, drained and rinsed

1 (15-ounce) can red beans, drained and rinsed

8 tablespoons fat free sour cream (optional)

PREPARATION

1. In a large pot, heat oil over medium heat.

2. Sauté onion, bell pepper, and garlic until tender, about 5 minutes.

3. Add tomatoes, corn, vegetable broth, chili powder, oregano, and beans. Stir well.

4. Cover and simmer until thoroughly heated, about 15 minutes.

5. Spoon into 8 bowls. If desired, top each bowl with one tablespoon of fat free sour cream and serve with whole grain rolls.

Makes 8 servings. *1½ cups per serving.*
Prep time: 10 minutes **Cook time:** 20 minutes

Nutrition information per serving: Calories 220, Carbohydrate 42 g, Dietary Fiber 11 g, Protein 11 g, Total Fat 2 g, Saturated Fat 0 g, Trans Fat 0 g, Cholesterol 1 mg, Sodium 482 mg

Recipe courtesy of BOND of Color.

Catfish Stew

Catfish stew and whole wheat rolls combine for a tasty and filling meal.

INGREDIENTS

3 cups water

1 teaspoon salt

2 medium white potatoes, peeled and cut into cubes

1 (14½-ounce) can diced tomatoes

1 cup chopped onion

4 cloves garlic, finely chopped

½ small head cabbage, chopped

1 pound catfish, cut into 1-inch chunks

1 tablespoon Soulful Seasoning (see recipe on page 34)

PREPARATION

1. In a large pot, bring water, salt, potatoes, tomatoes, onion, and garlic to a boil over medium-high heat. Reduce heat and simmer for 10 minutes.

2. Add cabbage and bring back to a boil. Reduce and simmer for 5 minutes.

3. Add catfish and Soulful Seasoning. Simmer until the catfish is cooked through, about 5 minutes more. Serve while hot.

Makes 6 servings. *1½ cups per serving.*
Prep time: 10 minutes **Cook time:** 20 minutes

Nutrition information per serving: Calories 198, Carbohydrate 21 g, Dietary Fiber 4 g, Protein 18 g, Total Fat 5 g, Saturated Fat 1 g, Trans Fat 0 g, Cholesterol 57 mg, Sodium 541 mg

Chicken Vegetable Creole

Serve with brown rice and salad for a complete meal. To add spice to this dish, try sausage instead of chicken.

INGREDIENTS

nonstick cooking spray

1 pound boneless, skinless chicken breasts, cut into large chunks

1 large onion, chopped

1 (14½-ounce) can diced tomatoes

⅓ cup tomato paste

2 stalks celery, chopped

1½ teaspoons garlic powder

1 teaspoon onion powder

½ teaspoon salt

¼ teaspoon red pepper flakes

⅛ teaspoon ground black pepper

1½ cups broccoli florets

Preparation

1. Spray a large skillet with nonstick cooking spray and heat over medium heat.

2. Add chicken and onion; cook, stirring frequently, for 10 minutes.

3. Stir in all remaining ingredients except broccoli and cook for 5 minutes, stirring occasionally.

4. Stir in broccoli, cook for 5 minutes more. Serve while hot.

Makes 6 servings. *1 cup per serving.*
Prep time: 10 minutes **Cook time:** 20 minutes

Nutrition information per serving: Calories 143, Carbohydrate 11 g, Dietary Fiber 3 g, Protein 19 g, Total Fat 3 g, Saturated Fat 1 g, Trans Fat 0 g, Cholesterol 46 mg, Sodium 460 mg

BBQ Turkey in Pepper Shells

These peppers will fire up your taste buds.

INGREDIENTS

¾ pound lean ground turkey

1 large onion, peeled and chopped

1 medium green bell pepper, seeded and chopped

1 (14½-ounce) can no salt added diced tomatoes

1½ cups low-sodium canned black beans, drained and rinsed

½ cup prepared barbecue sauce

1 teaspoon garlic powder

1 teaspoon liquid smoke

3 bell peppers (any color)

PREPARATION

1. Brown ground turkey in a medium skillet over medium-high heat until no longer pink; drain excess fat.

2. Add onion and cook until tender, about 5 minutes.

3. Add all remaining ingredients except the whole bell peppers; simmer for 10 minutes over medium heat.

4. Meanwhile, cut the whole bell peppers in half lengthwise and remove the seeds. Place in a microwave safe dish with a small amount of water.

5. Cover and microwave bell peppers on high until crisp-tender, about 5 minutes.

6. Remove peppers from dish and place on a large plate. Spoon turkey mixture into bell pepper shells and serve.

Makes 6 servings. *1 stuffed bell pepper shell half per serving.*
Prep time: 10 minutes **Cook time:** 25 minutes

Nutrition information per serving: Calories 209, Carbohydrate 28 g, Dietary Fiber 7 g, Protein 17 g, Total Fat 4 g, Saturated Fat 1 g, Trans Fat 0 g, Cholesterol 38 mg, Sodium 404 mg

Chicken and Dumplings

Add variety by using fresh carrots, broccoli, and zucchini when in season.

INGREDIENTS

2¼ cups canned low-sodium chicken broth

¼ cup water

1 medium onion, peeled and chopped

4½ cups frozen mixed vegetables (corn, peas, carrots, and green beans)

2 cups cooked and chopped chicken

1 teaspoon dried thyme

1¼ cups reduced fat prepared baking mix

⅓ cup lowfat milk

1 egg

PREPARATION

1. In a large pot, combine chicken broth, water, onion, vegetables, chicken, and thyme.

2. Cover and bring to a boil over medium-high heat. Reduce heat and simmer for 15 minutes.

3. Place baking mix in a small bowl. Remove 2 tablespoons and stir into pot to thicken the stew.

4. Add milk and egg to remaining baking mix and stir with a fork to blend. Drop rounded tablespoons onto hot chicken mixture. Cook over low heat, uncovered, for 5 minutes.

5. Cover and cook for 5 minutes more. Serve while hot.

Makes 6 servings. *1¼ cups per serving.*
Prep time: 10 minutes **Cook time:** 25 minutes

Nutrition information per serving: Calories 226, Carbohydrate 24 g, Dietary Fiber 3 g, Protein 21 g, Total Fat 5 g, Saturated Fat 1 g, Trans Fat 0 g, Cholesterol 74 mg, Sodium 362 mg

Turkey Chili

Serve with cornbread and salad for a hearty meal.

INGREDIENTS

nonstick cooking spray

1 pound lean ground turkey

1 medium onion, chopped

1 green bell pepper, chopped

1 (28-ounce) can whole
   tomatoes

2 (14½-ounce) cans kidney
   or pinto beans, drained and
   rinsed

1 (8-ounce) can tomato sauce

1 package chili seasoning

2 teaspoons ground black
   pepper

PREPARATION

1. Spray a large skillet with nonstick cooking spray and heat over medium-high heat.

2. Brown ground turkey until no longer pink; drain excess fat.

3. Add onion and bell pepper and cook for 5 minutes.

4. Add remaining ingredients. Cover and cook for 20 minutes over low to medium heat. Serve while hot.

 Makes 12 servings. *1 cup per serving.*
Prep time: 10 minutes **Cook Time:** 30 minutes

Nutrition information per serving: Calories 176, Carbohydrate 23 g,
Dietary Fiber 6 g, Protein 15 g, Total Fat 3 g, Saturated Fat 1 g,
Trans Fat 0 g, Cholesterol 25 mg, Sodium 503 mg

Recipe courtesy of American Cancer Society.

Oven Fried Catfish with Stir-Fry Greens

This tasty twist on a traditional dish will have your family asking for more.

INGREDIENTS

nonstick cooking spray

1 pound catfish fillets, cut into 6 equal pieces

4 teaspoons Soulful Seasoning (see recipe on page 34)

½ cup egg substitute

1½ cups cornmeal

1 teaspoon vegetable oil

¼ cup chopped onion

2 cloves garlic, finely chopped

1 pound collard greens, chopped

PREPARATION

1. Place an oven rack on the bottom level of the oven. Preheat oven to 400°F.

2. Spray a baking sheet with nonstick cooking spray.

3. Sprinkle both sides of fish with Soulful Seasoning.

4. Dip fish into egg substitute and roll in cornmeal.

5. Arrange fish on a baking sheet so that the pieces do not touch. Bake for 20 minutes.

6. Reduce heat to 350°F and bake until crust is golden and fish flakes easily, about 5 minutes more.

7. While the fish is baking, heat oil over medium heat in a large skillet.

8. Sauté onion and garlic until tender, about 3 to 5 minutes.

9. Add collard greens and cook, stirring often, until they turn bright green and limp.

10. Serve each piece of fish alongside one cup of greens.

 Makes 6 servings. *1 piece of fish and 1 cup of greens per serving.*
Prep time: 15 minutes **Cook time:** 30 minutes

Nutrition information per serving: Calories 282, Carbohydrate 32 g, Dietary Fiber 4 g, Protein 23 g, Total Fat 7 g, Saturated Fat 1 g, Trans Fat 0 g, Cholesterol 57 mg, Sodium 98 mg

Stir-Fry Greens adapted from recipe courtesy of Cut 'n Clean Greens.

Macaroni and Cheese with Glazed Vegetables

Try using sharp Cheddar cheese to kickup the flavor in this family favorite.

INGREDIENTS

2 cups uncooked macaroni noodles

nonstick cooking spray

½ cup chopped onions

¾ cup evaporated skim milk

1 egg, beaten

½ teaspoon ground black pepper

1¾ cups shredded lowfat Cheddar cheese

4 cups frozen mixed vegetables (corn, carrots, lima beans, peas, green beans)

1 teaspoon grated orange peel

½ cup 100% orange juice

1 tablespoon Dijon-style mustard

1 teaspoon low-sodium soy sauce

PREPARATION

1. Cook the macaroni noodles according to the package directions; drain and set aside.

2. Place an oven rack in the middle of the oven. Preheat oven to 350°F.

3. Spray a skillet with nonstick cooking spray and heat over medium heat.

4. Add onions to skillet and sauté until tender, about 3 minutes.

5. Add evaporated milk, egg, ground black pepper, and 1½ cups cheese; mix until smooth.

6. Add cooked macaroni noodles to the cheese sauce and stir until well coated.

7. Spray a casserole dish with nonstick cooking spray.

continued on following page

 Makes 5 servings. *1 cup macaroni and ¾ cup vegetables per serving.*
Prep time: 15 minutes **Cook time:** 30 minutes

Nutrition information per serving: Calories 457, Carbohydrate 73 g, Dietary Fiber 10 g, Protein 27 g, Total Fat 6 g, Saturated Fat 2 g, Trans Fat 0 g, Cholesterol 52 mg, Sodium 597 mg

Macaroni and Cheese with Glazed Vegetables *(continued)*

PREPARATION

8. Pour the mixture into the casserole dish and sprinkle the top with the remaining ¼ cup cheese.

9. Bake for 25 minutes or until the top bubbles and begins to brown.

10. While the macaroni and cheese is baking, cook mixed vegetables in a microwave safe dish according to the instructions on the package.

11. Combine the remaining ingredients in a small bowl and stir until well blended.

12. Drain vegetables and toss with the orange juice mixture.

13. Serve 1 cup of macaroni and cheese alongside ¾ cup of glazed vegetables.

Makes 5 servings. *1 cup macaroni and ¾ cup vegetables per serving.*
Prep time: 15 minutes **Cook time:** 30 minutes

Nutrition information per serving: Calories 457, Carbohydrate 73 g, Dietary Fiber 10 g, Protein 27 g, Total Fat 6 g, Saturated Fat 2 g, Trans Fat 0 g, Cholesterol 52 mg, Sodium 597 mg

Macaroni and Cheese adapted from recipe courtesy of National Heart Lung and Blood Institute.

Makes 6 servings. *1 piece of chicken and 1 cup squash per serving.*
Prep time: 10 minutes **Cook time:** 45 minutes

Nutrition information per serving: Calories 185, Carbohydrate 17 g,
Dietary Fiber 3 g, Protein 21 g, Total Fat 4 g, Saturated Fat 1 g,
Trans Fat 0 g, Cholesterol 46 mg, Sodium 202 mg

Oven Fried Chicken with Summer Squash

This dish is a great way to bring the family to the table.

INGREDIENTS

1 cup finely crushed cornflakes

¼ teaspoon salt

½ teaspoon ground black pepper

1 teaspoon onion powder

1 teaspoon garlic powder

½ cup evaporated skim milk

1 pound chicken breasts, skin removed and cut into 6 pieces

nonstick cooking spray

½ tablespoon vegetable oil

1 clove garlic, finely chopped

2 medium zucchinis, cut into short strips

3 medium yellow squash, cut into short strips

1 teaspoon dried oregano

PREPARATION

1. Place an oven rack in the middle of the oven. Preheat oven to 350°F.

2. In a small bowl, combine cornflakes, salt, ground black pepper, onion powder, and garlic powder.

3. Place evaporated milk in a separate bowl. Dip chicken pieces in milk and roll in crushed cornflake mixture, lightly coating both sides.

4. Spray a roasting pan with nonstick cooking spray and arrange chicken pieces on the pan in a single layer. Bake for 30 minutes.

5. While the chicken is baking, heat oil in a medium skillet over medium-high heat.

6. Sauté garlic in oil for about 3 minutes. Add zucchini, yellow squash, and oregano; continue to cook until tender, about 5 to 7 minutes.

7. Serve each piece of chicken with 1 cup of zucchini and yellow squash mixture.

Spotlight On: California Greens

Collard greens date back to prehistoric times and are one of the oldest members of the cabbage family. Collards are also known as tree cabbage. They are a cool-season vegetable, and are rich in vitamins and minerals that help prevent and fight disease.

Today, many varieties of greens --beet, chard, collard, kale, mustard, turnip-- continue to be a traditional staple in African American culture offered at potlucks, picnics, parties, and family dinners.

One cup of cooked greens is an excellent source of vitamin A, vitamin K, vitamin C, fiber, and calcium. Depending on the type of greens, one cup can also be a source of folate, iron, magnesium, potassium, riboflavin, vitamin B6, and vitamin E.

For more recipes and information about greens visit Cut 'n Clean Greens at www.cutncleangreens.com.

See the following recipes contributed by Cut 'n Clean Greens:

Vegetable Brunch Pie on page 19
Stir-Fry Greens on page 46
Swiss Chard Pinwheel Bread on page 53–54
Zucchini Muffins on page 61

Beet Greens   Swiss Chard   Collard Greens   Kale   Mustard Greens   Turnip Greens

Cornbread with Spicy Blackeye Peas

Serve with Oven Fried Chicken for a family dinner.

✳ ✳ ✳ ✳ ✳ ✳ ✳ ✳ ✳ ✳ ✳ ✳ ✳ ✳ ✳ ✳

INGREDIENTS

6 cups water

1½ (16-ounce) package frozen
   blackeye peas

1 cup cornmeal

1 cup all-purpose flour

¼ cup sugar

1 tablespoon baking powder

1 egg, beaten

¼ cup vegetable oil

1 cup lowfat buttermilk

1 cup frozen corn, thawed

   nonstick cooking spray

1 medium onion, chopped

2 cloves garlic, finely chopped

1 jalapeño pepper, seeded and
   chopped (optional)

PREPARATION

1. Place an oven rack in the middle of the oven. Preheat oven to 425°F.

2. In a medium-size pot, bring water to a boil over high heat.

3. Add blackeye peas and return to a boil. Lower the heat to medium and simmer for 30 minutes.

4. While the blackeye peas are cooking, mix cornmeal, flour, sugar, and baking powder in a medium bowl.

5. Add the egg, oil, buttermilk, and corn to the flour mixture. Mix ingredients until just blended (there may be a few small lumps).

6. Spray a 9 x 9-inch square pan with nonstick cooking spray.

7. Pour the batter into the pan.

8. Bake 20 to 25 minutes or until a wooden toothpick inserted in the center comes out clean.

9. As the cornbread continues to bake, drain the blackeye peas and keep half a cup of cooking water.

Makes 9 servings. *3-inch square piece of cornbread and ½ cup blackeye peas per serving.*
Prep time: 10 minutes **Cook time:** 50 minutes

Nutrition information per serving: Calories 329, Carbohydrate 54 g, Dietary Fiber 7 g, Protein 12 g, Total Fat 8 g, Saturated Fat 1 g, Trans Fat 0 g, Cholesterol 25 mg, Sodium 203 mg

continued on following page

Cornbread with Spicy Blackeye Peas (continued)

PREPARATION

10. Spray a skillet with nonstick cooking spray and sauté onions and garlic over medium heat until tender, about 3 minutes.

11. Add blackeye peas, jalapeño pepper, and reserved cooking water to the skillet and continue to simmer and stir for 5 minutes more.

12. Serve a square of cornbread over ½ cup of blackeye peas.

Makes 9 servings. *3-inch square piece of cornbread and ½ cup blackeye peas per serving.*
Prep time: 10 minutes **Cook time:** 50 minutes

Nutrition information per serving: Calories 329, Carbohydrate 54 g,
Dietary Fiber 7 g, Protein 12 g, Total Fat 8 g, Saturated Fat 1 g,
Trans Fat 0 g, Cholesterol 25 mg, Sodium 203 mg

Swiss Chard Pinwheel Bread

Discover the rich flavor of Swiss chard or use your favorite kind of greens.

INGREDIENTS

nonstick cooking spray

2½ cups (about 6 ounces) sliced mushrooms

¼ cup chopped onion

4 cups (about 12 ounces) chopped Swiss chard

1 tablespoon water

¾ teaspoon garlic powder

⅛ teaspoon ground black pepper

⅛ teaspoon salt

2 tablespoons grated Parmesan cheese

1 (10- to 13-ounce) can refrigerated pizza crust dough

¾ cup shredded part–skim Mozzarella cheese

1½ cups marinara sauce

PREPARATION

1. Place an oven rack in the middle of the oven. Preheat oven to 350°F.

2. Spray a skillet with nonstick cooking spray and heat over medium heat.

3. Add mushrooms and onion and sauté until tender, about 5 minutes.

4. Add Swiss chard and water. Continue cooking until Swiss chard becomes tender, about 8 to 10 minutes (you may need to add another tablespoon or more of water if the Swiss chard sticks to the skillet).

5. Add the garlic powder, ground black pepper, and salt.

6. Remove the skillet from the heat and stir in Parmesan cheese. Set the skillet aside to cool.

7. On a lightly floured board or surface, roll out pizza dough into a 10 x 14-inch rectangle.

Makes 8 servings. *2-inch slice per serving.*
Prep time: 20 minutes **Cook time:** 1 hour

Nutrition information per serving: Calories 193, Carbohydrate 31 g, Dietary Fiber 3 g, Protein 8 g, Total Fat 5 g, Saturated Fat 2 g, Trans Fat 0 g, Cholesterol 5 mg, Sodium 573 mg

continued on following page

Swiss Chard Pinwheel Bread *(continued)*

PREPARATION

8. Spread cooled Swiss chard mixture and Mozzarella cheese on top of dough, leaving about 1-inch of dough around the edges.

9. Starting from the long side, roll up the crust to make one large loaf.

10. Pinch along the seam of the loaf to seal and fold the ends under the loaf.

11. Place the loaf on a baking sheet sprayed with nonstick cooking spray.

12. Bake for 40 minutes or until golden brown.

13. Remove from oven and let cool for 5 minutes.

14. Cut into 8 slices and serve with warmed marinara sauce.

Makes 8 servings. *2-inch slice per serving.*
Prep time: 20 minutes **Cook time:** 1 hour

Nutrition information per serving: Calories 193, Carbohydrate 31 g,
Dietary Fiber 3 g, Protein 8 g, Total Fat 5 g, Saturated Fat 2 g,
Trans Fat 0 g, Cholesterol 5 mg, Sodium 573 mg

Adapted from recipe courtesy of Cut 'n Clean Greens.

Nellie's Kale Stew

A tasty stew anytime of the year.

INGREDIENTS

1 tablespoon vegetable oil

1 large onion, chopped

2 cloves garlic, chopped

1 medium green bell pepper, chopped

1 (8-ounce) can tomato sauce

1 (6-ounce) can tomato paste

1 (14-ounce) can low-sodium chicken broth

4 cups water

1 pound kale, chopped

2 medium carrots, chopped

2 medium white potatoes, cut into cubes

nonstick cooking spray

½ pound turkey kielbasa, sliced into thin rounds

PREPARATION

1. In a large pot, heat oil over medium-high heat.

2. Sauté onion, garlic, and bell peppers until tender, about 5 minutes.

3. Add tomato sauce, tomato paste, chicken broth, water, kale, carrots, and potatoes. Cook on medium-high heat until potatoes are tender, about 45 minutes.

4. Spray a medium skillet with nonstick cooking spray. Sauté kielbasa until heated through, about 5 minutes.

5. Add turkey kielbasa to stew and cook for 15 minutes more. Serve while hot.

Makes 10 Servings. *1½ cups per serving.*
Prep time: 10 minutes **Cook time:** 1 hour and 10 minutes

Nutrition information per serving: Calories 127, Carbohydrate 18 g, Dietary Fiber 3 g, Protein 7 g, Total Fat 4 g, Saturated Fat 1 g, Trans Fat 0 g, Cholesterol 12 mg, Sodium 596 mg

Recipe courtesy of BOND of Color.

Fresh, frozen, and canned fruits and vegetables are all good options that can make eating fruits and vegetables year-round easier to do. Buy fresh fruits and vegetables in season when they are cheapest to help stretch your food dollars. However, winter months are limited in the variety of fruits and vegetables that are available at low prices. Frozen and canned fruits or vegetables packed in their own juice can be an inexpensive and time-saving way to stay on track with eating the recommended amount of fruits and vegetables every day throughout the year.

BENEFITS

- Research shows that recipes made with frozen or canned fruits and vegetables have similar nutritional values to those made with fresh fruits or vegetables.

- Canned fruits and vegetables are "cooked" prior to packaging, so they are recipe ready.

- Frozen fruits and vegetables require little preparation—washing and slicing, is already done.

- Most frozen and canned fruits and vegetables are processed within hours of harvest, so they keep their flavor and nutritional value.

TRY THIS!

- Substitute frozen or canned fruits and vegetables for fresh fruits and vegetables in recipes.

- Try microwaving vegetables or buying pre-cut fruits and vegetables to save time.

- Read food labels to avoid canned and frozen foods that are high in salt, sugar, and other unwanted ingredients.

Snacks & Desserts

Spotlight On: California Sweet Potatoes

Fresh sweet potatoes are delicious, and their flavor blends well with herbs, spices, and flavorings. Whether sliced, diced, shredded, mashed, or served whole, their bright orange color jazzes up any plate.

Sweet potatoes with orange flesh are often called yams but they are not the same! Sweet potatoes are roots (like carrots) that are native to Central America and Peru, while true yams are tubers (like potatoes) that are native to Africa and can grow to be over 50 pounds.

It is believed that the confusion started in 1930 when growers began calling a new type of orange flesh sweet potato the Louisiana Yam to set it apart from the common white flesh sweet potato.

One medium sweet potato is an excellent source of vitamin A and a source of fiber, vitamin B6, and potassium.

For more tips and recipes on sweet potatoes, visit the Sweet Potato Council of California at www.cayam.com.

See the following recipes, made with California Sweet Potatoes:
Sweet Potato Hash on page 17
Sweet Potato Fries on page 30
Sweet Potato Apple Bake on page 64

Watermelon Salsa

A mouthwatering combination of sweet and zesty.

Citrus Berry Ice

A refreshing treat to beat the summer heat.

Makes 8 servings.
½ cup per serving.
 **Prep time:** 15 minutes

INGREDIENTS

3 cups seeded and
chopped watermelon

½ medium onion, chopped

½ red bell pepper, chopped

1 tablespoon seeded and
chopped jalapeño pepper

2 tablespoons chopped
fresh cilantro

2 tablespoons lime juice

1 teaspoon vegetable oil

PREPARATION

1. In a medium bowl, mix all
ingredients.

2. Serve immediately or cover
and refrigerate for up to
1 hour to allow flavors to
blend.

Nutrition information per serving: Calories 28,
Carbohydrate 6 g, Dietary Fiber 1 g, Protein 1 g,
Total Fat 1 g, Saturated Fat 0 g, Trans Fat 0 g,
Cholesterol 0 mg, Sodium 2 mg

Makes 4 servings.
1 cup per serving.
Prep time: 50 minutes

INGREDIENTS

2 tablespoons fresh lemon
juice

1 tablespoon sugar

2 oranges, peeled and
quartered

2½ cups fresh strawberries

¼ teaspoon cinnamon

PREPARATION

1. Place all ingredients in
a blender container and
blend until smooth.

2. Pour the mixture into a
shallow plastic container
and place in the freezer.

3. Stir every 15 minutes
until the mixture reaches
a sherbet-like thickness.
Serve immediately.

Nutrition information per serving: Calories 105,
Carbohydrate 27 g, Dietary Fiber 5 g, Protein 1 g,
Total Fat 0 g, Saturated Fat 0 g, Trans Fat 0 g,
Cholesterol 0 mg, Sodium 4 mg

Honey Gingered Fruit Salad

Dress up your fruit salad with a sprinkling of chopped almonds for a sweet and crunchy treat.

INGREDIENTS

1 large mango, peeled and cut into chunks

1 cup fresh blueberries

1 small banana, peeled and sliced

1 cup strawberries

1 cup seedless green grapes

1 cup nectarines, sliced

1 cup kiwifruit, peeled and sliced

Honey Ginger Sauce:

⅓ cup 100% orange juice

2 tablespoons lemon juice

1 tablespoon honey*

⅛ teaspoon ground nutmeg

⅛ teaspoon ground ginger

PREPARATION

1. In a large bowl, combine fruit.

2. In a small bowl, mix all honey ginger sauce ingredients until well blended.

3. Pour honey ginger sauce over fruit and toss together.

4. Refrigerate for at least 20 minutes and serve chilled.

Makes 6 servings. *1 cup per serving.*
Prep time: 10 minutes **Marinate:** 20 minutes

Nutrition information per serving: Calories 124, Carbohydrate 32 g, Dietary Fiber 4 g, Protein 2 g, Total Fat 1 g, Saturated Fat 0 g, Trans Fat 0 g, Cholesterol 0 mg, Sodium 4 mg

* Do not give honey to children under the age of one.

Recipe courtesy of BOND of Color.

Zucchini Muffins

A treat the whole family will love.

INGREDIENTS

- nonstick cooking spray
- 2 eggs
- ½ cup applesauce
- ¼ cup granulated sugar
- 1 teaspoon vanilla extract
- 1¼ cups whole wheat flour
- ¼ teaspoon salt
- 1 teaspoon baking soda
- 1½ teaspoons ground cinnamon
- ½ teaspoon ground ginger
- ¼ teaspoon ground cloves
- 2 cups grated zucchinis (about 2 small zucchinis)
- ½ cup raisins
- ⅔ cup toasted and chopped pecans or walnuts

PREPARATION

1. Place an oven rack in the middle of the oven. Preheat oven to 350°F.

2. Spray muffin pan (12 muffin cups total) with nonstick cooking spray and set aside.

3. In a large bowl, stir together eggs, applesauce, granulated sugar, and vanilla extract.

4. In a separate bowl, stir together flour, salt, baking soda, cinnamon, ginger, and cloves.

5. Stir flour mixture into egg mixture until just barely blended (there may be a few small lumps).

6. Gently stir in zucchinis, raisins, and nuts.

7. Divide batter evenly among muffin cups.

8. Bake 20 minutes or until a wooden toothpick inserted in the center of a muffin comes out clean.

9. Remove muffin pans from oven and let muffins stand for 5 minutes.

10. Remove muffins from pan and place them on a wire rack to finish cooling. Serve warm or at room temperature.

Adapted from recipe courtesy of Cut 'n Clean Greens.

 Makes 12 servings. *1 muffin per serving.*
Prep time: 15 minutes **Cook time:** 25 minutes

Nutrition information per serving: Calories 142, Carbohydrate 21 g, Dietary Fiber 3 g, Protein 4 g, Total Fat 5 g. Saturated Fat 1 g, Trans Fat 0 g. Cholestero 35 mg, Sodium 168 mg

Oven Fried Plantains

Impress your friends with this sweet Caribbean dish.

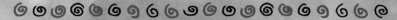

INGREDIENTS

nonstick cooking spray

4 very ripe medium plantains

⅛ teaspoon ground nutmeg

4 tablespoons brown sugar

PREPARATION

1. Place an oven rack in the middle of the oven. Preheat oven to 425°F.

2. Spray cookie sheet well with nonstick cooking spray.

3. Peel and slice each plantain into 16 thin diagonal slices.

4. Sprinkle plantains with nutmeg and brown sugar.

5. Bake until crisp, about 45 minutes. Serve while warm.

Makes 8 servings. *8 slices per serving.*
Prep time: 5 minutes **Cook time:** 45 minutes

Nutrition information per serving: Calories 158, Carbohydrate 42 g, Dietary Fiber 3 g, Protein 1 g, Total Fat 0 g, Saturated Fat 0 g, Trans Fat 0 g, Cholesterol 0 mg, Sodium 8 mg

Mixed Berry Crisp

This medley of flavors will tantalize your taste buds.

INGREDIENTS

7 cups frozen mixed berry medley, thawed

½ tablespoon sugar

1 tablespoon all-purpose flour

1½ teaspoons cornstarch

nonstick cooking spray

¾ cup old fashioned oats

¼ cup whole wheat flour

¼ cup packed brown sugar

¼ teaspoon salt

¼ teaspoon cinnamon

⅛ teaspoon vanilla extract

2 tablespoons chilled butter, cut into small pieces

PREPARATION

1. Place an oven rack in the middle of the oven. Preheat oven to 375°F.

2. In a medium bowl, mix berries, sugar, all-purpose flour, and cornstarch.

3. Spray a 9 x 9-inch baking dish with nonstick cooking spray. Pour fruit mixture into the baking dish.

4. In a medium bowl, combine oats, whole wheat flour, brown sugar, salt, cinnamon, and vanilla extract. Mix in butter until crumbly.

5. Sprinkle oat mixture evenly over berry mixture.

6. Bake until topping is golden brown, about 45 minutes. Serve warm or at room temperature.

Makes 6 servings. *1 cup per serving.*
Prep time: 10 minutes **Cook time:** 45 minutes

Nutrition information per serving: Calories 244, Carbohydrate 48 g, Dietary Fiber 11 g, Protein 5 g, Total Fat 6 g, Saturated Fat 3 g, Trans Fat 0 g, Cholesterol 10 mg, Sodium 235 mg

Sweet Potato Apple Bake

Serve with frozen yogurt for a special treat.

INGREDIENTS

1 pound sweet potatoes
(about 1 large sweet potato),
peeled and cut into chunks

⅔ cup unsweetened 100%
apple juice

2 apples, peeled and cut into
chunks

½ teaspoon vanilla extract

1 tablespoon butter, melted

½ teaspoon cinnamon

½ teaspoon nutmeg

2 tablespoons brown sugar

nonstick cooking spray

PREPARATION

1. Place an oven rack in the middle of the oven. Preheat oven
   to 400°F.

2. In a large bowl, mix all ingredients.

3. Spray a 9 x 9-inch glass baking dish with nonstick cooking spray.
   Pour mixture into baking dish.

4. Bake until sweet potatoes are tender, about 45 minutes. Spoon the
   liquid in the dish over the sweet potatoes and apples a few times
   while baking. Serve while warm.

Makes 6 servings. *½ cup per serving.*
Prep time: 15 minutes **Cook time:** 45 minutes

Nutrition information per serving: Calories 121, Carbohydrate 25 g,
Dietary Fiber 3 g, Protein 1 g, Total Fat 2 g, Saturated Fat 1 g,
Trans Fat 0 g, Cholesterol 5 mg, Sodium 37 mg

Adapted from recipe courtesy of Glory Foods.

Families have many activities to choose from when planning a reunion, but the traditional barbecue at the park is an all time favorite. No matter what type of gathering your family chooses, chances are food will play a big role in the celebration. Reunions are a good time to try new, healthy dishes and teach loved ones how to lead healthier lifestyles, such as eating colorful fruits and vegetables and being active every day.

BENEFITS

- Eating healthy and being active are key to preventing and managing type 2 diabetes, high blood pressure, heart disease, and keeping a healthy weight.

- Making healthy food choices as a family helps build lasting habits that can protect the health of family members for many years to come.

- Introducing relatives to small changes in diet and physical activity can make a big difference in their lives and help them stay on track at family gatherings.

TRY THIS!

- Serve fruit salads and grilled vegetables at picnics and barbecues.

- Start a healthy recipe contest to encourage loved ones to try new dishes. Give everyone copies of the top recipes.

- Organize activities such as group walks, games, or sports to inspire loved ones to be healthier throughout the reunion.

- Dance - form a dance line or do the electric slide. Younger family members can join in and teach other family members current dance steps.

Cookbook Evaluation Form

Your feedback is important to us. Please answer the questions below and return the survey to the address listed on the back cover of this cookbook, attention *African American Campaign*.

How many recipes have you tasted from the cookbook? _____

How many recipes have you prepared from the cookbook? _____

On a scale from 0 to 6 (0 = Very Poor, 3 = No opinion, 6 = Excellent), how would you rate the cookbook on the following:

Usefulness..0 1 2 3 4 5 6

Recipes include foods you usually eat...0 1 2 3 4 5 6

Recipes helped you to try new foods..0 1 2 3 4 5 6

Cooking instructions are clear and easy to follow..0 1 2 3 4 5 6

Ingredients are affordable..0 1 2 3 4 5 6

How likely are you to recommend this cookbook to a family member or friend? 0 1 2 3 4 5 6

Cookbook Evaluation Form *(continued)*

List the two recipes you like the most.

_____

_____

What do you like about these recipes? _____

_____

_____

List the two recipes you like the least.

_____

_____

What don't you like about these recipes? _____

_____

_____

Comments:

_____

_____